PHOT

Learning in

ACTIVITIES

Photocopiable activities for

Personal and Social Development

Hannah Mortimer

Author
Hannah Mortimer

Editor
Sally Gray

Assistant editor
Clare Miller

Series designer
Joy White

Designer
Sarah Rock

Illustrations
Cathy Hughes

Cover photo
Martyn Chillmaid

Published by Scholastic Ltd, Villiers House, Clarendon Avenue,
Leamington Spa, Warwickshire CV32 5PR

© 1998 Scholastic Ltd   Text © 1998 Hannah Mortimer
1 2 3 4 5 6 7 8 9 0   8 9 0 1 2 3 4 5 6 7

British Library Cataloguing-in-Publication Data
A catalogue record for this book is available from the British Library.

ISBN 0-590-53878-0

Contents

Introduction

The Desirable Outcomes for Personal and Social Development

In this book you will find activities which help children play and learn in all the areas of personal and social development specified by the School Curriculum and Assessment Authority in their publication *Desirable Outcomes for Children's Learning*. The ideas can also be applied equally well to the pre-school curriculum guidance documents for Wales, Scotland and Northern Ireland.

Developing personal and social skills

Each of the chapters in this book concentrates on developing a different aspect of the personal and social curriculum from getting on with others to exploring feelings and emotions.

In the first chapter, 'Gaining confidence' the children are given opportunities to develop confidence and self-respect and are encouraged to feel proud of their own achievements. These experiences serve to underpin the rest of the curriculum and naturally feed into the subsequent chapters where children are helped to develop friendships with other children, while feeling supported and encouraged by the adults who look after them.

The activities in this book also provide children with opportunities to play on their own and in groups of different sizes, encouraging them to persevere and concentrate for longer periods. In addition there are activities to encourage co-operation and problem-solving, and to develop independence.

Children also need help to become more sensitive to the needs and feelings of others and there are activities which help them to talk about and consider other points of view. It is also important that children grow up with an understanding and appreciation of the cultural diversity that exists within our society and there are activities to help them learn about other cultures and beliefs and to respond to cultural and religious events in their communities.

How to use the photocopiable activities

Within each activity chapter, you will find two pages of activity notes and the corresponding photocopiable activity sheets. Use these sheets flexibly, adapting them to suit your group and each individual child. Some sheets will be most useful if they are enlarged on the photocopier. You can also photocopy onto coloured paper, or mount the photocopies onto colourful card to make them eye-catching.

Mounting the children's completed work can be a useful way of showing them how much you value their contributions and of developing a sense of achievement.

Some of the activity sheets can be used by individual children and others are designed to be used by pairs or small groups of children working together. Once completed, you will find that some can be kept as a record of assessment, or held in the child's personal portfolio. These can be a useful addition to your evidence when preparing for an inspection, showing the wide range of activities which you have carried

out with the children in the area of Personal and Social Development. If you are gathering evidence of a child's special educational needs then you may find the completed activity sheet a useful addition to your monitoring and planning.

Using resources

Use a wide range of materials to complete the activity sheets. Some will suit paint, some collage, some bright pens, some involve cutting out, and still others can be mounted and used as talking points or as part of a game. You will find that the activity sheets relate to a wide range of play activities and take you into every area of your space and every kind of play activity. This is particularly important since children's personal and social development pervades every area of play, learning and relating to others.

Working with parents

Use the activity sheets to keep in touch with parents in a variety of ways. Some can be completed at home and at times the completed sheet can be sent home as a way of sharing the day's activity and encouraging praise and further activity at home. At other times the sheets can be used ahead of an activity as a way of inviting families to send in items of interest relating to the topic.

How to use this book

You will find that this book follows on naturally from the previous publication *Learning in the Early Years – Personal and Social Development* by Hannah Mortimer (Scholastic) extending the activities and providing further resources. In the previous book, you will also find practical suggestions for planning, assessment and record-keeping. You can either use this activity book in conjunction with the previous book, or it can stand on its own as a useful resource for your personal and social curriculum.

The six activity chapters follow the same headings as in the previous book: 'Gaining confidence', 'Learning to learn', 'Becoming independent', 'Getting on with others', 'Feelings', and 'Social worlds'.

About this series

In the *Learning in the Early Years Series*, you will find books on supporting children's learning in each of the Areas of Learning in the Desirable Outcomes: Personal and Social Development, Language and Literacy, Mathematics, Knowledge and Understanding of the World, Physical Development and Creative Development. Each of these books also has a sister publication with additional ideas and photocopiable activities.

A further book in the series, *Ready for Inspection* provides practical down-to-earth guidance on all the management issues that groups will need to take on board in order to deliver the outcomes effectively and prepare for a successful inspection.

chapter one

Gaining confidence

The eight activities in this chapter aim to make the children feel welcomed, settled and valued in the group. The children will also develop skills of working with a partner and learn to identify with the larger group.

PAGE 9

Warm welcome
Learning objective
To feel encouraged and supported when settling into the group.
What to do
Learn about the needs and preferences of each new child that joins your group by sharing this sheet with parents before the child begins. Adapt the sheet to suit your particular situation and use it to talk through any concerns with parents.

PAGE 10

Portrait gallery
Learning objective
To feel a valued member of the group and to identify with it.
What to do
Sit with groups of up to four children and explain that you are going to make a big wall picture together. Pass round a hand-held mirror and encourage the children to talk about their hair, eye colour and the clothes they are wearing. Provide each child with an activity sheet and a selection of colouring and collage materials to use to make a picture of themselves. Mount the 'children' onto a large frieze, adding details of your playroom to make it interesting. Write each child's name beneath their picture on the frieze.

PAGE 11

My day
Learning objective
To talk about group activities with the family.
What to do
Sit with each child at the end of a session and look through the activity sheet together. What activities has the child taken part in within that session? Help them to circle the appropriate pictures and talk about each activity as

you do so. Let the children take the sheet home with them and encourage them to talk to their parents about what they have been doing. You can also use the sheet at the start of a session to help individual children plan what they would like to do.

Well done! PAGE 12
Learning objective
To develop pride in achievements and share this with people at home.
What to do
Use the activity sheet to celebrate a particular achievement. Present it to the child and make sure that they and their parents know why it has been given. Encourage parents to pin up the certificate at home and celebrate it too. Make sure every child receives one each half-term, for a variety of reasons.

PAGE 13

Lily pads

Learning objective

To play confidently with a partner.

What to do

Use this activity with an even number of children, up to a maximum of ten. Photocopy the sheet, enlarging to A3-size if possible. Give each child a sheet to paint, talking together about lily ponds, frogs and ideas for suitable colours. Allow the paint to dry. Help the children cut round the shapes and place them all on an open floor. Play some music, inviting the children to hop around like frogs. Explain that when the music stops they must find a friendly frog to share a lily pad with!

PAGE 14

All my own work

Learning objective

To collect favourite pieces of work and to develop pride in personal achievements.

What to do

Fold a piece of A1 sugar paper into a pocket with a flap, to make an art portfolio for each child. Staple or stick down the sides. Working in groups of four, invite the children to decorate the activity sheet to form a label to stick onto their folder. Provide a range of coloured pens, glue sticks, tinsel, and shiny shapes for the children to use. The portfolio can be used as a running record of the child's creations and may be taken home at the end of term.

PAGE 15

Two's company

Learning objective

To work effectively with a partner.

What to do

Set up the play activities shown on the sheet. Gather together an even number of children (up to a maximum of ten). Use the activity sheet as a talking point about which games and toys are best played with on your own, and which are more fun when played with someone else. Help the children pair up with partners and ask them to choose an activity from the sheet which they can play together. When they have finished let them colour the relevant picture. Return to play a different partner game another day.

PAGE 16

Favourite things

Learning objective

To talk about and appreciate favourite things, to be listened to and to feel valued.

What to do

Send this activity sheet home with the children and encourage parents to talk with their child, fill in the answers and return it to the group. Sit down in a circle with ten to twelve children and use the sheets as a starting point to talk about favourite things. Show that you value all the children's choices and encourage them to share their experiences and preferences with each other.

Warm welcome

Please fill in this sheet with your child. It will help us to welcome your child to the group as well as helping them to settle in.

My full name is _____

I like to be called _____

In my family the grown-ups are called _____

_____

I already know these children in the group _____

_____

My favourite toy is _____

I like to play _____

My favourite story is _____

I still need help with _____

_____

These things worry me _____

_____

I am looking forward to _____

_____

Portrait gallery

Make this child look like you.

My day

Draw a circle around the activities you have done today.

Well done!

...has done *really well* today because...

Signed:_____

Date:_____

We're really proud of you!

Lily pads

Paint and cut out the lily pads.

All my own work

Decorate this label to stick onto your folder.

This folder belongs to:

Two's company

Which toys do you play with on your own?

Which are more fun if you play with someone else?

Favourite things

Please talk with your child and let us know some of their favourite things.

My favourite cuddly toy is _____

My favourite story is _____

My favourite toy to play with is _____

My favourite thing to eat is _____

My favourite television programme is _____

_____

My favourite outing is _____

I like to play with these children best _____

_____

The best thing I remember is _____

_____

chapter two

Learning to learn

The activities in this chapter will develop skills of looking, listening, concentrating and remembering. There are also opportunities to help children co-ordinate what they see with what they do and to build on their understanding of abstract concepts.

PAGE 19

Fishing game

Learning objective

To concentrate when listening and to remember a short sequence of words.

What to do

Work with groups of up to six children. Make a 'fishing rod' for each child with a small magnet attached to the end of a piece of string tied to a stick or pencil. Give a copy of the sheet to each child. Help them to colour and cut the pieces out. Put a paper-clip onto each shape. Arrange the shapes on a table and invite each child to catch 'a *boot* and then a *kettle*'. See if they can remember the correct order. Change the objects and the order, gradually building up to three.

PAGE 20

Washing lines

Learning objective

To concentrate when looking and to copy a given sequence.

What to do

Work with a small group of four children at a table. Provide an assortment of colouring materials and ask the children to colour in the clothes on the sheet. Help them to cut out the pieces. Fix a paper-clip to each piece of clothing and arrange two 'washing lines' of string for each child, suspended across a frame, one beneath the other. Working in pairs, help one child to hang up their washing on the line. Challenge the second child to hang theirs up in the same order, providing help if necessary. Repeat the process with the children swapping roles. Older children may be able to copy the order even if the clothes lines are side-by-side.

PAGE 21

Concentration

Learning objective

To persevere with a repetitive task for a surprise result.

What to do

Work with small groups of up to four children sitting round a table. Give each child a copy of the sheet and help them to colour the flowers. Fold each sheet of paper along the solid line. Provide scissors and help each child to cut along the dotted line, taking care not to stray. When they have finished, make the final snips along the bold straight line for them and allow the child to open up the paper with a surprise result! Encourage the children to wear their garlands of flowers if they wish to.

PAGE 22

Folding up

Learning objective

To concentrate and persevere when using fine finger movements.

What to do

Help the children use mark-making, copying over or drawing to make a letter to a friend on the blank side of the activity sheet. Help them to fold it neatly along the dotted lines and write the friend's name on the outside. Make a cardboard posting box for all the letters. Share out the letters at the end, making sure each child receives one.

Snake sequences

PAGE 23

Learning objective
To copy a given sequence when using collage materials.
What to do
Enlarge a copy of the activity sheet to A3-size for each child. Arrange a selection of collage materials on a table; pasta, sequins, pulses, cotton wool, coloured string pieces, paper shapes, and enough glue and stickers for each child. Encourage them to choose a different collage material for each section of the snake. Now challenge them to copy the same sequence on their second snake so that they have 'identical twins'. Arrange the snakes on a giant frieze and challenge the children to find the matching pairs. The children could work on this activity in pairs if they prefer.

Jigsaw

PAGE 24

Learning objective
To make and complete a simple jigsaw.
What to do
For each child copy the sheet onto card, or mount onto card with glue. Provide a range of pens and crayons and invite each child to colour in the picture. Help them to cut the jigsaw out, then send it

home in an envelope for the child to share with the people at home. To extend the activity make double-sided jigsaws by asking the children to draw a picture onto the back of their sheet before cutting it out.

Listening lotto

PAGE 25

Learning objective
To listen to and identify a series of familiar sounds.
What to do
Make a recording of all the sounds shown on the sheet. Sit groups of up to eight children around a table in a quiet space. Provide each child with six bricks or counters and a copy of the sheet. Play back the recording, inviting the children to place a brick on each sound as they hear it.

Opposites

PAGE 26

Learning objective
To identify simple opposites and talk about what makes them different.
What to do
Sit with a group of up to four children around a table. Give each child an activity sheet and talk about the pictures as a group. Ask each child in turn to show you which of the pictures is high, low, big, small, long, short, heavy, light, empty and full. Make a note of any concepts which a child does not know and find practical opportunities for teaching these.

18

Fishing game

Colour and cut out.

Washing lines

Colour and cut out.

Concentration

FOLD

FOLD

Folding up

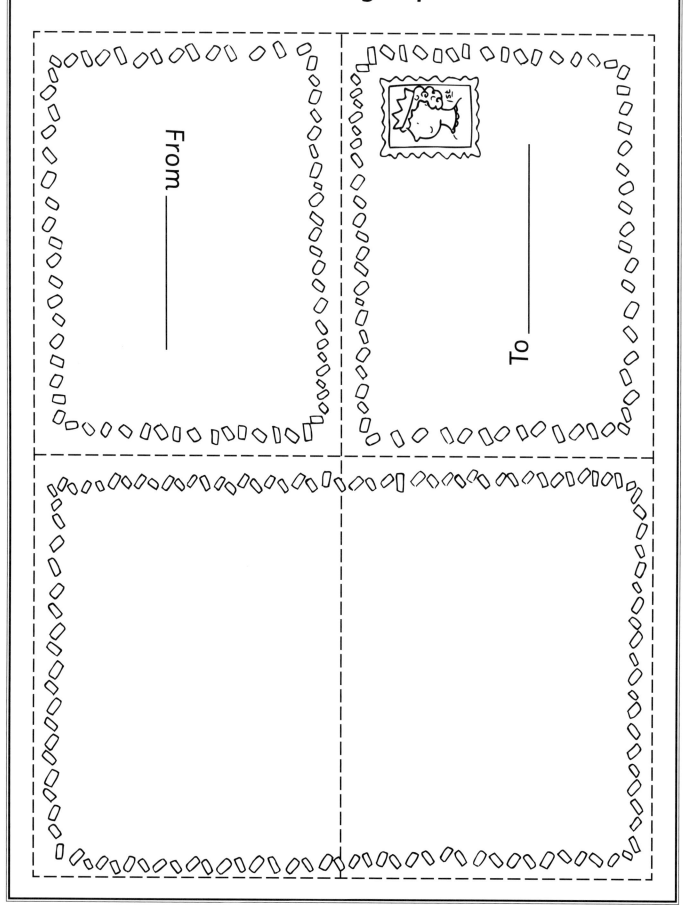

From _____

To _____

Snake sequences

Make both your snakes look exactly the same.
Now cut them out.

Jigsaw

Colour and cut out.

Personal and Social Development

Listening lotto

Cover up the sounds when you hear them.

doorbell

traffic

washing

stairs

water

telephone

Opposites

Talk about the opposites you can see.

chapter three

Becoming independent

In this chapter the children will be encouraged to develop greater independence in their work and play and in looking after themselves. They will take part in a broad range of activities that cover topics such as preparing for school, shopping and safety in the home.

PAGE 29

What next?
Learning objective
To develop the ability to choose independently.
What to do
Copy two activity sheets onto thin card or stick the sheets onto pieces of card. The symbols represent the different activities available in the group. With the children's help add some more of your own. Cut the squares out and mount a small piece of Velcro onto the back of one of the sets. Arrange them onto a felt board. Use the other set to label your activities around the room. Make a name card with Velcro on the reverse for each child.

Introduce the symbols at circle time and let the children pass them round. Help each child to decide what to do next, placing their name card onto the board next to the symbol of their choice.

PAGE 30

Please help me!
Learning objective
To learn to be independent.
What to do
Copy an activity sheet for each parent and invite them to use it to tell you how independent their child is at home and which skills they still need help with. Explain that this information will help you to develop the independence skills required by their child and that it doesn't matter if their child still needs a lot of help. Use the answers to make sure you are teaching and encouraging the children who need it, providing just the right amount of help for each child to do as much as possible by themselves. Praise all the children's efforts to be independent.

PAGE 31

Healthy food
Learning objective
To talk about food which keeps us healthy.
What to do
Enlarge the activity sheet and use it at 'circle time' as a talking point. Which foods are good for you? Which do you like to eat? Which are good for your teeth and bones? Which help you to stay healthy? Which give you energy to run about? Use the sheet as a starting point for a wall frieze, encouraging children to cut out pictures from old magazines to add to the 'Healthy Food' picture.

Follow up the activity by enlisting the parents' help to arrange a healthy picnic or feast. Ensure that foods from a variety of cultures and traditions are included in the feast.

27

PAGE 32

Staying safe
Learning objective
To think about staying safe at home.
What to do
Give each child a copy of the activity sheet to take home. Encourage parents to talk about hazards around the home, and to help their child to colour over or circle all the dangers in the picture. As a group, follow up with a discussion about keeping the play area safe, and encourage the children to develop their own ideas for sensible rules and precautions.

of each of the items on the list all by themselves. Praise their concentration and encourage them to persevere with the task. When they have finished, ask them to come and show you. Repeat the activity with different items and let the pairs of children swap over roles.

Ready for school

PAGE 34

Learning objective
To think and talk about the different independence skills needed for school.
What to do
Use this activity with each child who is due to go to school next term. Talk to them individually about the skills shown, and invite the child to show them off to you. When they have done so successfully, let them colour the relevant pictures in.

PAGE 33

Going shopping
Learning objective
To work co-operatively on a problem-solving task with a partner.
What to do
Look at the objects on the activity sheet and make sure you have several of each item kept in their usual places around the play area. Copy enough sheets for half your number of children. Help each child find a partner and explain that they are going to go 'shopping' together around the room. Give one child a basket to carry and the other child the list. Explain that they need to find one

28

What next?

Add some more symbols in the empty squares.

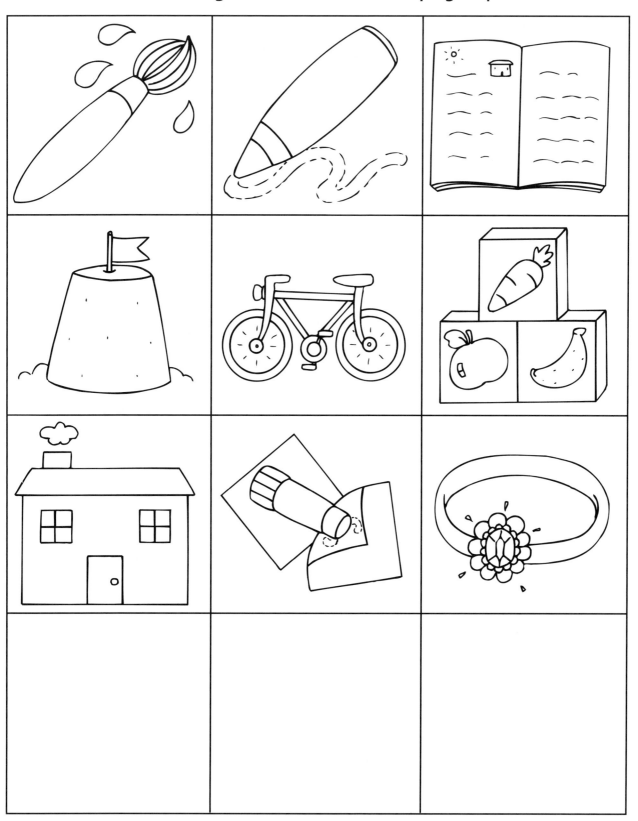

Personal and Social Development

Please help me!

Please help us to help your child become more independent by telling us
how much help is needed at home. Remember — we're here to help!

Name of child _____

How much help does your child need with:

• managing their own coat _____

• going to the toilet _____

• washing hands _____

• pouring a drink _____

• taking shoes on and off _____

• managing buttons _____

• eating with a knife and fork _____

Is there anything else you feel your child should be doing which you would
like us to help with?

Healthy food

Staying safe

Colour in or circle the dangers that you can see in this picture.

Going shopping

Look at the pictures. Try to find one of each of these things and put it in your basket.

Ready for school

These are all the things I have learned to do ready for school!

chapter four

Getting on with others

Try these activities that will encourage the children to make friends, take turns, share and think about others. The children will play games and make reward badges and thank-you cards as they develop these important life skills.

PAGE 37

Me and my friend
Learning objective
To talk about favourite things with another child.
What to do
Use this activity with groups of two children. Photocopy an activity sheet for each pair of children, enlarging to A3-size if possible. Gather a selection of six toys, sweets, small objects, and pictures of activities cut out from magazines and catalogues. Help each pair of children to look at the items and place them in the appropriate section of the hearts, depending on whether one of them likes it or both do. Talk to the children about the results.

PAGE 38

All smiles
Learning objective
To learn to share and to be kind to other people.
What to do
Copy the activity sheet for each child. Prepare a table with colouring materials, scissors, circles of card the same size as the badges, sticky pads, and glue sticks. Help the children to colour the badges, cut them out, glue them onto cardboard circles and make them into badges with sticky pads. Notice how the children are working and explain that you are looking to see if they are sharing with each other and if they are taking care with their work. Give each child a badge to wear and to take home. Put the rest into a box.

In future sessions, reward children for good behaviour by telling them why you are pleased and presenting them with a badge. Try to find an opportunity for rewarding every child over a period of time.

PAGE 39

Hoses and ladders
Learning objective
To learn to take turns with one other child.
What to do
Copy the sheet onto card. This game can be played by two children who will need your help to understand and follow the rules. Adapt a large dice by adding a sticker to each face with one, two or three dots on it. Teach the children how to play by throwing the dice and moving the correct number of spaces. If they land on a square with a ladder, they can move up to its other end. If they land on a hose, they must slide down.

PAGE 40

Tea-time
Learning objective
To learn how to share out between three.
What to do
Photocopy the activity sheet for each child. Working at a table with groups of up to six children, help them to colour and cut out the bowls, spoons and place mats. Arrange three bears on the table and ask each child in turn to share out the items so that each bear has one of each in front of it. Have the teddies shared fairly?

PAGE 41

Being friends
Learning objective
To talk about all the things that friends do.
What to do
Use 'circle time' to talk about friends. How do you know that someone is being friendly? Talk about sharing, playing together, being kind and not hurting

each other. Encourage the children to think of their own examples. Give each child a copy of the activity sheet to take home and ask the parents to help their child to look for the children who are being friendly in the picture.

PAGE 42

Thank-you

Learning objective
To think about a kindness and say 'thank-you' with a card.

What to do
This activity is best done after a festival or anniversary involving presents, or when the group would like to say 'thank-you' to a special visitor. Copy the activity sheet onto thin card if possible. Encourage the children to decorate and colour it adding their own original picture, name and message to the inside. Talk about the different pictures on the back of the card.

PAGE 43

Baby care

Learning objective
To think about all the care that a new baby needs.

What to do
Invite one of your parents with a young baby to come in to visit the group. Ensure that the baby has had its inoculations so as not to put it at risk of infection. Ask the adult to bring in some of the items needed to look after the baby; a nappy, a bottle, a blanket, a soft toy. Encourage the children to ask questions and to share their own experiences. Copy the activity sheet for each child to take home and use as a stimulus for talking about the visit of the parent and baby.

Pairing up

PAGE 44

Learning objective
To work co-operatively with several other children.

What to do
Work in groups of seven children. Photocopy the activity sheet, mount onto card and cut into six sections. Draw a second set, with mirror images of the first. Put one set in a box and give the other set out, one to each child. Now invite six children to stand in a circle with their picture hidden behind their backs. Ask the seventh child to pick a picture out of the box. Whose picture does it match? Help the child move round the circle asking to see each child's picture in turn, with a 'please' and a 'thank-you'. When they find the match, they keep the pair and the new child becomes the seeker.

Me and my friend

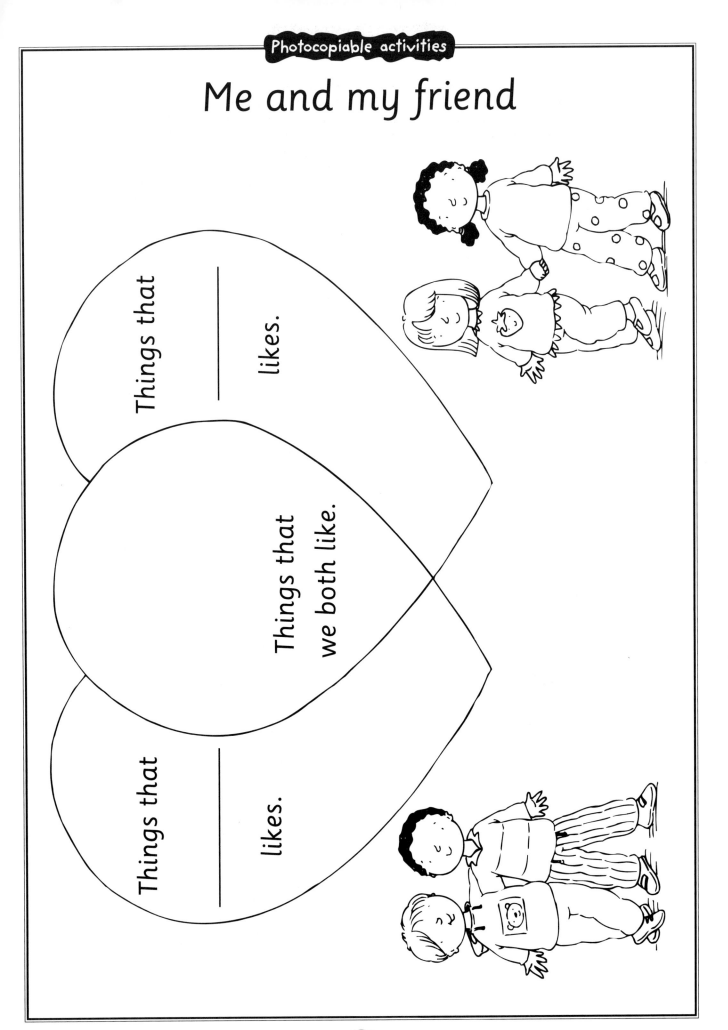

Things that _____ likes.

Things that we both like.

Things that _____ likes.

All smiles

Colour and cut out these pictures to make badges.

Hoses and ladders

Play this game with a friend.

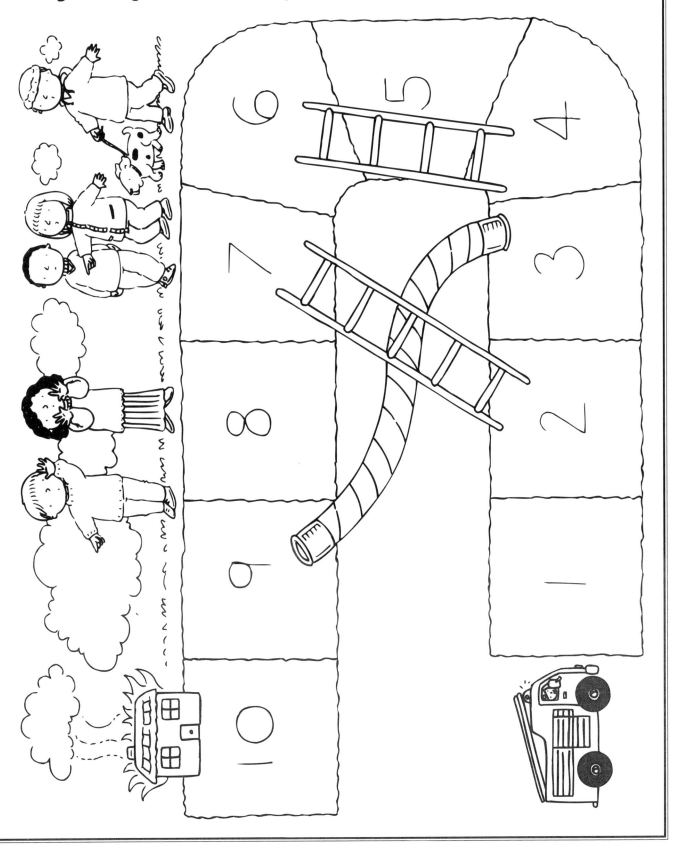

Tea-time

Colour and cut out for a sharing game.

Being friends

Which children are being friendly in this picture?

How do you know?

Thank-you

FOLD HERE

Learning in the Early Years - Photocopiable Activities

Personal and Social Development

Baby care

What things does a new baby need?

Pairing up

Cut out the cards and use them for a pairing game.

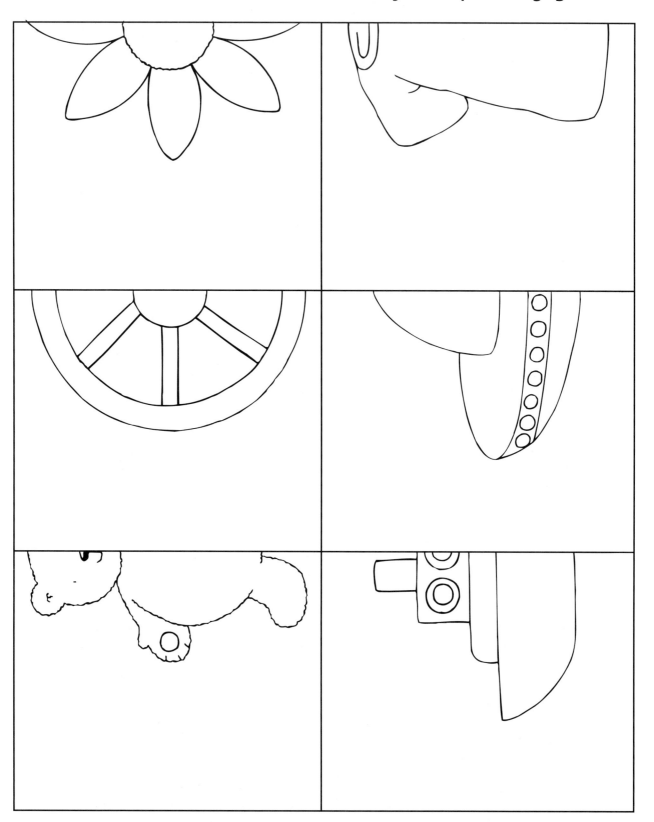

chapter five

Feelings

The ideas in this chapter focus on helping the children to recognize and express their feelings appropriately. The activities use a wide range of stimuli and resources including music and pictures and there are suggestions for ways to involve the children's families.

PAGE 47

Happy face, sad face

Learning objective

To talk about happy and sad things.

What to do

Use this activity in groups of up to six children. Photocopy a sheet for each child. Help them to draw an arrow from each picture to the happy or sad face. Talk about things which make you happy or sad.

PAGE 48

Making it better

Learning objective

To think about difficult or unhappy situations and how to make them better.

What to do

Enlarge the picture to A3-size so that a group of children can look at it together. Ask the children what is happening in the pictures, and what each of the children shown might be thinking. What might happen next to make everything better again? Encourage the children to think of all the different points of view and to come up with good ideas for helping.

PAGE 49

Putting it down

Learning objective

To express feelings through drawings.

What to do

Choose two contrasting pieces of music – one loud and angry and one calming and smooth. Provide each child with a photocopy of the activity sheet (enlarged to A3-size if possible).

   Play the children short pieces of the music and ask them how the two types make them feel. Then explain that you would like them to draw some pictures to match the music. Which picture frame will they choose for which music? Provide a selection of colouring

materials and play the music again while the children express their feelings by drawing inside the frames. Create a wall display of 'angry' and 'calm' pictures.

How does it feel?

PAGE 50

Learning objective

To consider other children's feelings.

What to do

Show a small group of children the activity sheet. Make up a story to go with it; think of a name for the boy and talk about what he was planning to do before his tractor was broken. Now describe the accident that led up to the damage; perhaps his friend tripped over it when he wasn't looking. What could the friend do to make things better? Now invent a new twist to your story; supposing the friend *meant* to do it. How would each child feel? What does it mean to be *friendly*?

45

PAGE 51

Cross-patch!

Learning objective

To talk about how everyone feels cross sometimes, and to consider appropriate ways of expressing this.

What to do

Photocopy the activity sheet and send one home with each child. Explain to parents that you are talking about feelings this week, and ask them to sit down with their child and complete the sheet using the child's own words. Back at the group use the sheets to talk about these feelings in small groups. Who else feels cross when this happens? How do *you* show that you are cross? Is this a good way to do it? How does it make other people feel? What could we do instead? Keep the discussion supportive and encouraging.

PAGE 52

Body language!

Learning objective

To talk about how we use our bodies to tell people how we are feeling.

What to do

Photocopy a sheet for each child. Gather up to six children together round a table and give each child six bricks or counters. Invite them to look at the pictures and to cover up the one which looks sad. Then do the same for the ones which look cross, happy, frightened and so on. Follow up by inviting the children to make shapes with their bodies which show each of these feelings in turn. Praise all the children's attempts.

PAGE 53

Nonsense!

Learning objective

To talk about funny things and understand a visual joke.

What to do

Show the children the activity sheet and see whether they can spot all the funny things in the picture. Give each child a copy of the sheet to take home to show to their families, and invite the children to bring in a simple joke to share with everyone, sharing it with you first to check that it is suitable. Help the children see the double meanings that most jokes have in common, and enjoy the laughter together.

PAGE 54

Happy memories

Learning objective

To express wonder at a special occasion and share this with another person.

What to do

Provide each child with a copy of the sheet to take home. Encourage families to talk with their child about their happiest memories and to help them to fill in the sheets to bring back and share with the group.

Happy face, sad face

Draw arrows to the happy or the sad face.

Making it better

What is happening and how could we make it better?

Putting it down

Choose a picture frame to draw your angry and your calm pictures.

How does it feel?

How do you think the children in this picture are feeling?

Cross-patch!

Take this home to talk to your family about feeling cross.

• What sorts of things make *you* feel cross?

_____

• What do you do when you are feeling cross?

_____

• Do your friends or family feel cross sometimes too?

_____

• What kinds of things make them feel cross?

_____

• What makes you feel better when you are feeling cross?

_____

• Make a cross face and then make it happy again. Look in the mirror!

_____

Body language!

How do these people feel?

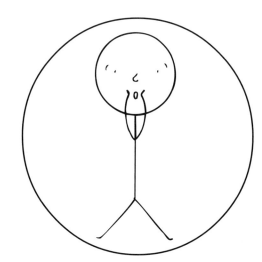

Nonsense!

Talk about the funny things you can see in this picture.

Happy memories

Talk with your family about the happiest things you can remember. Ask them to write them down using your words. Do you have a photograph you can bring in to share?

The three most wonderful things that ever happened to me were...

1. When _____

_____

_____

2. When _____

_____

_____

3. When _____

_____

_____

How did they make you feel?

chapter six

Social worlds

These eight activities will help children to learn and talk about many cultures and beliefs, and to find out more about their world and community. The final activity helps children to prepare for settling into school.

PAGE 57

Celebrations

Learning objective

To develop an understanding of time and celebrate anniversaries and festivals within the group.

What to do

Enlarge the activity sheet and mount it on card to form a wall calendar. Introduce it to the children at 'circle time' and use labels and Blu-Tack to place on it different anniversaries or festivals your group is planning to celebrate such as children's birthdays, Christmas and Diwali. Try to include all the important festivals for the children within the group. Ask parents to help you with suggestions and make sure you understand the significance of each religious occasion if you are unclear. Ensure that each child is included on your calendar in some way and remember to celebrate the day appropriately when it arrives.

Festivals of the year

PAGE 58

Learning objective

To talk about and mark a range of feasts and festivals from different cultures and beliefs.

What to do

Cut out the pictures from the activity sheet and ask the children to help to add colour to them. You can use them to stick to your calendar (see page 57) when a particular feast or festival day arrives.

Food, glorious food

PAGE 59

Learning objective

To talk about different types of food from a wide range of cultures.

What to do

Plan the session well ahead so that you can ask parents to help. Set up a table with a wide range of foods, and invite the children to sample and taste them. Provide each child with a sheet to take home and talk about. Suggest that they colour in their favourite foods or ones that they tasted at the group.

Meet the police

PAGE 60

Learning objective

To talk about how the police force helps people in the neighbourhood.

What to do

Arrange for someone from the local police force to visit your group. They will usually bring some special equipment to show the children. Help the children ask questions, and try to ensure that the presentation is kept simple and that the children have understood. Photocopy an activity sheet for each child to take home as a memento of the visit.

PAGE 61

Festival of light
Learning objective
To talk about light festivals in different cultures and religions.
What to do
Read about festivals of light in different religions such as the Hindu festival of Diwali, the Christingle candle at Christmas and the Jewish festival of Hanukkah. Invite members of the local faith communities to visit you and talk to the children about light in their tradition. Photocopy an activity sheet for each child, preferably onto thin card.

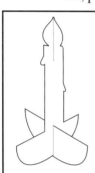 Working in small groups, help the children colour the candle on both sides, cut it out and slot the two sections together to form a three-dimensional model. Use the candles as part of a display about festivals of light.

PAGE 62

Praying together
Learning objective
To learn about how children and their families from other cultures and beliefs worship together.
What to do
Arrange a visit to the places of worship in your area, or invite the local religious leaders to visit and explain simply to the children how their communities worship and to show religious artefacts and pictures. Use the activity sheet as a talking point encouraging children who worship to share their experiences with others. Ensure that those children who do not practise a faith are given the chance to talk about other things they do with their families.

Children together
PAGE 63
Learning objective
To talk about what makes all children alike, whatever their appearance or culture.
What to do
Use this activity sheet as a stimulus picture to initiate a discussion about how each individual is special and unique yet all are children together. Who has dark hair? Who has long legs? Who has brown eyes? Who has long hair? Who likes playing? Who likes chips? Who likes watching television?

Our school
PAGE 64
Learning objective
To visit the receiving primary school and record the activities seen there.
What to do
Use this activity for all your children about to go into school. Copy the sheet for each child. Talk about all the activities which children do in school and arrange a visit there. When the children return, invite them to ring the activities they saw and take their sheet home to talk about.

Celebrations

	June		December	
	May		November	
	April		October	
	March		September	
	February		August	
January			July	

Festivals of the year

Colour, cut out and stick onto a festivals calendar.

Christmas

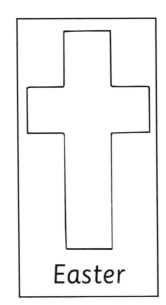

Easter

Diwali

Eid-Ul-Fitr

Chinese New Year

Hanukkah

Food, glorious food

Talk about the foods with an adult and colour in the things that you like.

Meet the police

Talk about this picture with an adult.

Festival of light

Colour, cut out and slot together to make your own candle.

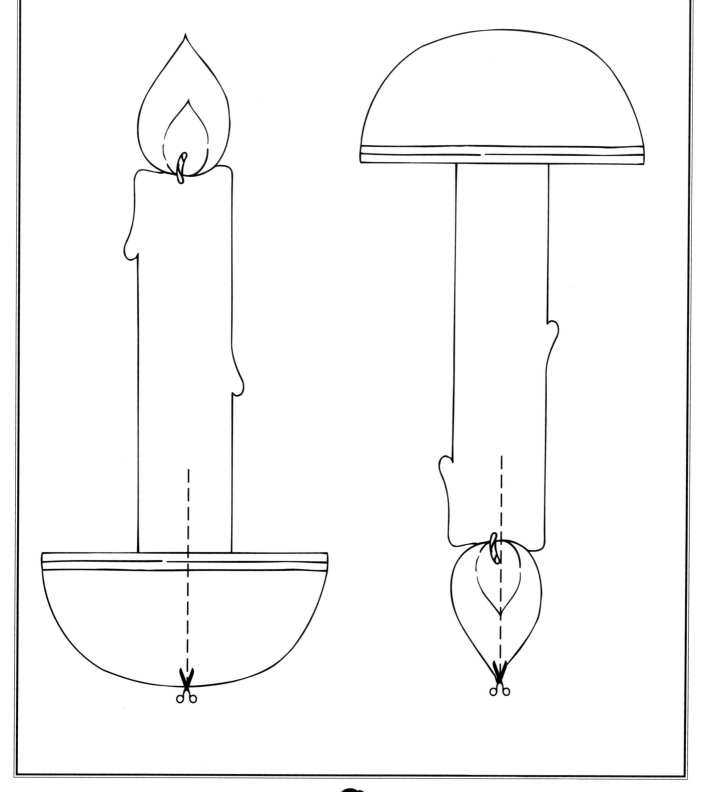

Praying together

What can you see in this picture. What things do you do with your family?

Children together

Talk with a friend. Tell them something that you like about them.

Our school

Put a ring round all the things you saw at the school.